Dental Claimsupport's

Ultimate Guide to

Dental Billing & Reporting

"*Ultimate Guide to Dental Billing and Reporting* provides a proven, accessible, and easy-to-implement dental billing template for any dental office. All practices will benefit from the simplicity and positivity of this important guide. I really like the actual number examples and the templates for how to structure your day. It's great information and a must-have for all dental offices."

— **DR. CHRISTOPHER COMER,** DMD FAGD, Savannah, GA

"If you want a roadmap to show you how to run the claims process for your dental practice, this book is a must-read. As a business coach who sees hundreds of processes firsthand each and every year, this book is as good a guide as any process I have seen. It is clear, practical, and to the point. Implement it to eliminate the billing chaos from your practice!"

— **GREGORY GRAY**, Leadership and Business Coach

"Ultimate Guide to Dental Billing and Reporting is an excellent resource for anyone in the field of dentistry. This book is designed for 'all of the dental team,' not just the administration team. Regardless, if you have been in dentistry for one year or 34 years (like I have been), this is excellent information. Dentistry changes continuously. I have a feeling a sequel will be coming out soon with lots of great and insightful updates!"

— TERRI HERROD WILSON, RDA, CDA, CDPMA, CDP, FADAA

"This book makes billing and insurance very easy to understand. It maps out a very concise approach to insurance and billing in the dental office. I have taken many CE courses on these topics over the years. This book not only gave a more complete picture of the billing and insurance process than I have seen previously but also gave an easy way to approach and implement the process in the dental office."

— DR. MICHAEL GROOVER, DMD

"Private practice is a challenge for every dental office. The dental world has changed from the days when a dentist could open an office, do great dentistry, and be paid a fair fee. Success is assured when the office finds the balance. Balancing the art, science, and business of dentistry is a challenge. Josh Smith has given us a 'road map' to help with the business aspect of dentistry when it comes to dental insurance. I am a fee-for-service office, but I still want my patients to get their max dental benefit. Following the suggestions made in this easy read will help your staff travel the road of the dental insurance road trip. WELL DONE.

— **JEFFREY C HOOS** DMD FAGD

"What a great training resource for insurance coordinators and managers alike. This book breaks down the claim process so that you can evaluate your own systems. It's full of actionable advice, so get your highlighter ready!"

— **TERESA DUNCAN**, MS,
   Odyssey Management, Inc.

"I think that this book is a good manual for understanding the billing and collection process in a dental office. I think it would be particularly helpful as a must-read for the front desk person(s) in charge of insurance claims and collections."

— **ANTHONY (SKIP) MOLLICA, JR**. DDS,
Associate Professor, Dental College of
Georgia at AU, Dept. of General Dentistry

Dental Claimsupport's

Ultimate Guide to

Dental Billing & Reporting

- **Learn the full dental billing process** from start to finish

- **Master key reports** for a smooth-running practice

- **Enjoy a dental practice** that's efficient and well-managed

Josh Smith

HIGH BRIDGE BOOKS
HOUSTON

Ultimate Guide to Dental Billing and Reporting
by Josh Smith

Printed in the United States of America
ISBN: 978-1-954943-21-6

High Bridge Books titles may be purchased in bulk for educational, business, fundraising, or sales promotional use. For information, please contact High Bridge Books via
www.HighBridgeBooks.com/contact.

Published in Houston, Texas by High Bridge Books

Contents

Preface

Running the front desk at any dental of-fice can be difficult, but it doesn't have to be. This stuff can be easy, seriously. The only reason it's difficult is because of bad business practices. Also people just "don't know what they don't know." It really is that simple.

In 2008, I was a super smart guy that graduated from the University of Georgia with a BA in *real estate*. I hope you read right through the sarcasm there … Thing is, graduating with that real estate degree is exactly what happened. After the market collapsed, there wasn't much for newbies looking for their first job out of school. And when I started looking for degree-related work, I kept striking out. It was brutal. One thing I didn't want to do was live back with the so-called "rents," so I knew I needed to figure something out.

A friend of mine, now business partner, Davy Clay, said he could help me get an interview. At the time, he was working for a small dental group out of Savannah, GA. He got into the dental field out of school because 1. he needed to pay bills (don't we all!), and 2. Davy graduated around the same time as I did, and nothing was readily available in his field. He was mainly doing administrative work with check-in and verification but quickly moved into the financials.

Once you see how dentists get paid and how an office *should* be run, you realize the potential that *every* office has. Davy quickly moved to be an office manager and saw that the office could be run more efficiently, the bottom line could be healthier, and ultimately money was being thrown out the window. So like any good operations manager, he dove in and figured it out.

He put together a dental billing process (the same billing process we use today at our outsourced dental billing company, Dental ClaimSupport) that ensured nothing would fall through the cracks. The whole patient experience, from walking through the doors to posting insurance claim payments, got buttoned up. A process existed for everything. The results were fantastic enough that the owner of the small dental group asked that Davy do an internal audit on all the practices under the group umbrella to figure out where and how the other practices might be lacking.

What did he find? Davy discovered that every office performed its dental billing differently. In most instances, he found that the office didn't even have a dental billing process put in place!

So yes, in the same company, with multiple dental offices, *every* office did its billing differently.

If this was the case in this small group, could it also be the case in independent dental offices across the country, other small groups, and dental service organizations (DSOs)?

Long story short, it was the case.

That's why we founded Dental ClaimSupport and set out to implement our process and proven method across the United States. Although we love what we do, we know it's impossible to have the opportunity to work with everyone. And honestly, outsourcing dental billing isn't necessarily appealing to all dentists and practice owners. However, dental billing needs to be done the right way for your office, for your patients, *and* (I can't believe I'm saying it) for insurance companies.

I wrote this book so you can understand:

- The exact roles and responsibilities of the front desk dental team

- The full dental billing process

- The key reports that indicate a profitable, smooth-running dental practice

Now is the time to liberate yourself from the chaos that many dental offices suffer through on a daily basis.

I know what you are about to read will greatly benefit your dental practice. The teachings in this book have transformed hundreds of dental offices into streamlined, money-making, patient-focused machines. I have watched it with my own eyes.

However, having the skills and the know-how is one thing, but having the time and personnel to perform the daily tasks is another. If, after reading this book, you feel you could benefit from the help of an outsourced dental billing company, I invite you to visit dentalclaimsupport.com to see how we can help.

BONUS: To download a free insurance verification, audit form, and other awesome bonus features from reading this book, please visit bonus.dentalbillingandreporting.com.

Introduction

Running a dental practice comes with a never-ending to-do list.

In this book, I will *not* be discussing things like marketing in your area, how to answer the phone, what alluring fragrance to keep in the bathroom, or how often you should be vacuuming and mopping the floors. All of that is part of running your dental office. But our focus in this book is your patient flow, using a dental billing process, and understanding your dental software reporting. This book focuses on operations and financials. It's structured in a systematic way to teach anyone how to run the front office, whether you have been in dentistry for 30 years or you're just starting out.

This will be your "how-to" guide, but you and your dental team will have to put in the work. Knowing how to do something is just the beginning, but once you start, don't quit. Keep repeating. That is all any process is, and dental billing is *all* about repetition. So take the next sentence seriously and make your decision.

If you believe you run a perfect dental practice, don't continue reading.

You are still here, so where do we start? What's the first thing that has to happen at the admin level of any dental practice? A patient calls and makes an appointment. Ding ding ding! But what happens next? A lot happens, but the dental billing process should remain the same *every time*.

The best way to simplify learning this process is to imagine your dental practice has only one patient. If you can handle this dental billing process for one patient per day, then you can handle it for 500 per day.

Well, 500 patients per day is extreme and would cause carpal tunnel, but you catch my drift. Following a process and making sure each task is completed will have you running a flawless dental practice in no time.

The dental billing process can be broken down into two phases. Phase one is the life-cycle of a dental patient. Phase two is the life-cycle of a dental claim.

Phase One: Life-Cycle of a Dental Patient

1. The patient makes an appointment and gives insurance and protected health information (PHI) to your office.

2. Your office enters the patient's PHI into the dental software.

3. Your dental team performs insurance verification before the patient is seen.

4. The patient is seen for the appointment and "walked out" after the visit.

Phase Two: Life-Cycle of a Dental Claim

1. Your dental team creates the insurance claim, and the claim is batched.

2. Using a clearinghouse, the dental claim is sent from the dental software to the insurance company.

3. The insurance company processes the claim and makes a payment to your office (via electronic funds

transfer [EFT], virtual credit card [VCC], or paper check).

4. Payment is posted in the patient ledger, which closes out the claim.

Congratulations! You are done! Thanks for reading!

Just kidding, but the simple flow above shows there really isn't much to the process. What's important is how to perform the necessary duties attached to each numbered item in the process.

I will go through each item individually, showing exactly how it needs to be handled daily. I will be discussing and demonstrating all subsets of each numbered item so you have a clear understanding of each item and how to accomplish them accurately and efficiently.

Many dental offices will say they have one to four employees handling this entire process. But who is responsible for what? Does one or two people handle the patient duties, meaning appointment, check-in, insurance verification, etc.? Does someone else take over during the life-cycle of the claim?

Introduction

Is it a free-for-all where whoever has a spare second tries to handle what needs to be completed? Not having a defined process will lead to lost revenue and claims falling through the cracks.

First things first, you need to have a structure. Confirm you know who is responsible for each step in the billing process. Each team member needs to be held accountable for his or her tasks.

Here we go! Strap in and get ready for an explanation of each step and the importance of a streamlined, continuous flowing dental billing process. Get ready to understand how implementing and following a dental billing process *will* lead to a healthier bottom line. Also, recognize how key reports in your software will train your eye to notice trends and see where deficiencies may lie.

Part 1

Steps of the Dental Billing Process

1

Life-Cycle of a Dental Patient

Phase One

1. Creating a Dental Appointment

This process is quite simple. Every dental practice management software has the ability to make appointments, and they all work similarly. A patient will call your office, contact your call center, or book an appointment online.

What's important is obtaining the patient's insurance information and demographic information during this initial contact. This information is *accurately* entered into your dental software, "creating" a patient if they haven't already been established, of course. Next is setting the appointment.

Hygiene appointments are usually seamless as most patients are coming in for a routine dental cleaning and checkup. However, if a patient is seeing the doctor, the scheduler needs to allot enough time during the appointment for the doctor to complete the work.

Most providers, dentists, and hygienists prefer appointments made that fit their schedule and structure. For example, some doctors prefer high production like crowns, implants, or bridges in the morning, and more basic procedures like fillings in the afternoon. This allows for a "flow" of sorts and predictability in the daily schedule.

Many providers also like when time is allotted for emergency patients and new patients. That isn't to say you will always have a new patient scheduled every day or that an emergency patient will call in, but being prepared will allow your office to service every patient.

Take a look at the sample appointment page on page 6. The appointment page has designated time ranges for certain categories of procedures. This makes it easy for your team to identify immediately what sort of procedure should be placed in what time slot. I recommend applying a color for each time range. Each color will signify a certain type of procedure or appointment type. See below for an easy example.

For Doctors

Time Range	Type of Procedure / Appointment Type	Suggested color
8am – 11:30am	High Production	Red
11:30am–12pm	Emergency Patients	Orange
1pm – 1:30pm	Emergency Patients	Orange
1:30 – Close	Low Production	Yellow
12pm – 1pm	Lunchbreak	Pink

For Hygienists

Time Range	Type of Procedure / Appointment Type	Suggested color
8am – 11:00am	Normal Hygiene	Green
11:00am–12pm	New Patients	Blue
1pm – 2pm	New Patients	Blue
2pm – Close	Normal Hygiene	Green
12pm – 1pm	Lunchbreak	Pink

This example appointment page is a recommendation that has worked for many providers. In this example, we have high production in the morning (**8am – 11:30am**), time slots around lunch for emergency patients (**11:30am–12pm, 1pm – 1:30pm**), and lower production procedures to round out the afternoon (**1:30 – Close**). For hygiene, we have normal hygiene throughout the day (**8am – 11:00am, 2pm – Close**) and time slots for potential new patients before and after lunch (**11:00am–12pm, 1pm – 2pm**).

First, make sure you understand how your own providers want their patients scheduled. Then, create your own scheduling. You will see this positively impact the day-to-day patient flow as well as the communication between the administrative and clinical teams. Do your best at the front desk to stick to this scheduling process, and your dentists and hygienists will *love* you. So will your patients!

2. Data Entry into Your Dental Software

The next steps in the dental billing process are entering the patient's PHI as well as performing insurance verification. In these steps, data entry must be correct. Inaccurately inputting patient information or insurance information will ensure your claim does not get paid. This is a no-no!

Inaccurate data entry could be anything from wrong dates of birth to misspelled patient names. It can also be on the insurance side, where insurance ID numbers, group numbers, or payer IDs are entered incorrectly.

This should be 100% avoidable. **Slow down!** Double-check that all data entry information is correct before moving on to another task or patient. This only takes seconds and can save you hours of headache in the future. Time is money.

This is the shortest section you'll read because it is cut and dry. Verify your data entry is accurate. It is the easiest way to make or break clean claim submission to insurance companies. Don't fall short in this step!

3. Insurance Verification: How to? What's the Importance?

The third step in the dental billing process is performing insurance verification. Insurance verification is defined as the process of checking a patient's insurance coverage and benefits prior to the date of service to ensure payment for services. Some people refer to this as "verifying insurance benefits." In a nutshell, insurance verification confirms the patient has active coverage. It also confirms what procedures are covered and how much will be paid by the insurance for each procedure you may perform.

Verification is typically done by visiting insurance web portals or calling the insurance carrier. For either way you choose, you need a "full breakdown" of benefits in order to truly understand a patient's coverage. You can utilize the insurance web portal or ask a representative on the phone for a full breakdown of benefits.

What is a full breakdown? This includes which dental procedures are actually covered benefits, at what percentage are they covered (for example, 100/80/50%), has the patient already used any benefits elsewhere, what is the patient's plan maximum, etc. Below is an example insurance verification sheet that can be used in any dental office.

DENTAL GIRL	Date Verified			
Patient Name	**Patient DOB**	**Subscriber**	**Subscriber DOB**	**Relationship to Subscriber?**
Member ID	**Insurance Co.**	**Effective Date**	**Calendar Year?**	
In Network?	**Deductible**	**Has it been used?**	**Ann. Max**	**Amount Used?**
Preventative %	**Procedure**	**Frequency**	**Eligible/History**	
	Exams (periodic D0120)			
	Prophy (or time limit D1110)			
	Bitewings (D0272 or D0274)			
	Pano or FMX (D0330 or D0210)			
	Fluoride (D1206)			
	Sealants (D1351)			
Basic %	**Procedure**	**% Percentage**		
	Extractions		Homograft Fees (composite)?	
	Endo		Any Waiting Period?	
	Perio (D4341/D4342)		Missing Tooth Clause?	
	Perio Maint. (D4910)		Notes:	
Major %	**Procedure**	**% or Frequency**		
	Crowns			
	Implants (D6010)			
Ortho %	**Covered? Age Limit?**	**Lifetime Max**		

In addition, you want to verify any frequency limitations, age limitations, and certain clauses such as waiting periods, missing tooth clauses, and replacement clauses. This information will allow you to collect from the patient up front, meaning before they leave the office after the dental visit. You know exactly what insurance will pay (without having to send a pre-determination) and exactly how much the patient will owe you (if you have successfully entered in your PPO fee schedule).

Don't let this sample insurance verification sheet intimidate you. While there is a lot of information to fill out, the form is not completed at every visit. Once you have this breakdown, as long as the patient keeps this same insurance plan, this data shouldn't change. If the plan changes, then yes, a new full breakdown is needed. To verify insurance effectively, consider these pro tips:

Insurance Verification Pro Tips

1. Always get a full breakdown for every new patient.

2. Always get a new breakdown if insurance coverage changes.

3. A family covered under the same policy will have the same breakdown of benefits as the guarantor or whoever purchased the insurance (it is not necessary to do individual breakdowns).

   a. For family members:

      i. Verify they are eligible.

      ii. Obtain the patient's history of procedures for frequency limitations and replacement clauses.

      iii. Obtain a dollar amount of any benefits that have already been used.

4. Returning patients with the same insurance only need to be verified that they still have the same coverage and are eligible (no full breakdown is needed again).

You can see that although you need full breakdowns of benefits for every patient, you will not have to go through the full process every single time.

Example One

If Jimmy comes into your office for his first new-patient visit, and you perform a full breakdown of benefits, you will not need to do that again when Jimmy returns in two weeks for his crown, filling, or whatever other treatment was planned. You just need to ensure Jimmy is still eligible under the same insurance.

Example Two

Jimmy's daughter comes in for her first visit. You already know her full breakdown (same as the dad's) and simply need to make certain she is eligible or has any history of procedures that may fall under frequency limitations.

Hopefully, you are seeing a pattern of efficiency. Insurance verification seems like a daunting task, and early on it may be, especially if you were never doing verifications in the first place. However, your office should/will get to the point where full breakdowns are only needed for new patients and patients who have had a change in coverage.

I have heard horror stories of two to three employees in a dental office taking all day to do insurance verifications for the next day of appointments. Of course, it all depends on the size of the office and the number of patients being seen, but here's an example to go by.

An office seeing 45–50 patients a day should only require one person doing insurance verification for roughly two hours.

Remember, efficiency is key with insurance verification. Work smarter:

- Use insurance web portals for full breakdowns and simple eligibility checks.

- Call the insurance if a web portal doesn't give good/complete break-downs.

- Group your patients together by insurance company for efficiency, whether you are using the web portal or calling.

- Get all the information the first time!

When Should You Perform Insurance Verifications?

Be proactive here. A good business practice is verifying benefits for patients two days (48 hours) before their scheduled appointment. A few reasons this is important:

1. You know they are eligible.

2. You know what the patient is coming in for, so you have a good idea of what will be owed by the patient or if you need to dig further and find out if an uncommon procedure is going to be covered.

3. You will have time to insert emergency patients into your schedule

You never know what's going to happen in a dental office. Patients can be finicky, to say the least. Some folks don't even think they need an appointment and elect to just "walk in" because they have a toothache. These are emergency patients.

Having already performed verification for all the other patients being seen that day, you will have the time to insert the emergency patients into your schedule and take care of them. You are not only building revenue, but you are also providing care to someone in need.

Having a toothache hurts like hell. Trust me, your emergency patient won't forget you, and you'll have made a patient for life.

Believe it or not, insurance verification is *not* done in many offices across the United States yet is *the single most important task you can perform in any dental office.* Why? Among many reasons (more on this later) is the "$0 balance system."

What Is the $0 Balance System?

If your dental team inputs all patient information into your practice management software correctly (data entry) and verifies your patient's benefits (insurance verification), you should not have any issue sending the patient's claim accurately. And as I briefly hit on earlier, you will know how much the insurance payer will cover. If you know how much will be covered by insurance, then you know exactly what the patient's out-of-pocket should be.

Collect the patient's out-of-pocket *before* the patient leaves the office after the visit. Once the claim pays, the patient is left with a $0 balance, a clean ledger, and you never have to send invoices to patients. Again, this saves time and money and is efficient. You can probably see a trend here ...

Failure to perform insurance verification leads to unpaid claims and lost revenue. Your dental team will also not be able to explain the patient's benefits should the patient ask. This leads to lower case acceptance and lost potential revenue.

The Golden Dental Rule = Always perform insurance verification for every patient.

4. Completing an Appointment for a Patient

Step four involves checking a patient in for an appointment and releasing the patient after the visit. As stated above, your dental team should have already created a digital chart for this patient with the personal and insurance information when they created the appointment. Your team should have also completed insurance verification, making sure the patient is active with insurance coverage and eligible to be seen by your dental providers.

You should know "what" your patient is being seen for that day in your dental practice. For example, is the patient coming in for a routine hygiene visit or seeing the doctor for some major work? Also, the patient could be an emergency or walk-in (unscheduled) patient. Regardless, after the patient completes the visit, verify that what was done in the dental chair matches what you have in your dental software and on the patient's ledger to be billed.

This will guarantee you send an accurate claim to the insurance carrier. Because you performed insurance verification and loaded the patient's benefits correctly in your dental software system, you will also know if the patient has any out-of-pocket expenses for the work completed that day. Remember, always collect the patient's out-of-pocket before the patient leaves.

Lastly, try to go ahead and confirm all patients have their next appointment scheduled. This could either be for future treatment presented to them that day, such as the need for a crown, or filling, etc. Or, it could simply be a patient's six-month recall visit. Either way, to avoid having to contact the patient again, be proactive and schedule the patient while they are in front of you. By doing this, you're not only locking in future potential revenue, but you're providing superior customer service as now this is one less thing the patient has to think about in their daily life.

2

Life-Cycle of a
Dental Claim

Phase Two

1. Creating and Batching a Dental Claim

The next steps in the billing process start the life-cycle of a claim. Your patient has already been seen, so now it's time to send the claim to insurance in order to get paid. All practice management software has the ability to create a claim from procedures completed that day.

Creating and batching a claim isn't complicated, and most practice management software work similarly. Batching a claim means putting it in queue to send later on with other batched claims. While checking out your patient, your front desk should always create and batch the claim. This will indicate how much is expected from insurance and how much is expected to be out-of-pocket from the patient.

Most dental teams elect to batch all claims throughout the day, then send them all together either at the end of the day or the next morning, as opposed to sending claims individually. Fewer amounts of claims transmission typically equal fewer issues with claim submission. Imagine seeing 100 patients with insurance in one day. Do you want 100 transmissions or one? Time is money.

Lastly, always have your providers, dentists, and hygienists look over their day-sheets before submitting all claims. Day-sheets are essentially reports that list the patients seen that day in the dental office and what procedures each patient had done.

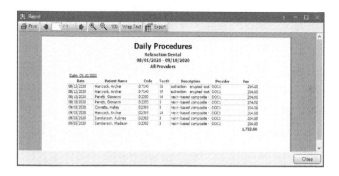

In order to send accurate claims to the insurance carriers, take a few seconds to confirm the procedures done for each patient are correctly documented.

Next, you submit the claim. How does this work exactly?

2. Claim Submission Through a Clearinghouse

All dental offices should be using a clearinghouse. What is a clearinghouse?[1]

Let's get technical. A clearinghouse is a private or public company that provides connectivity and often serves as a middleman between healthcare providers and payers.

Let's get simple. *Clearinghouses make sure that claims sent from your dental software are distributed to the correct insurance company electronically.*

So let's take the "100 claims with one transmission" example from the section above. All of these claims are transmitted to the clearinghouse. The clearinghouse makes sure information is correct with each claim, then sends each claim to the correct insurance company.

How does the clearinghouse know which insurance company is correct? Great question. The answer is payer IDs. Payer IDs are five-digit/alpha characters unique to each insurance company. Keep it simple please … okay!

Everyone loves a good sports analogy, right? Think of a clearinghouse as a football quarterback. Let's say, Tom Brady. Don't let this analogy make you hate clearinghouses, though …

Tom has a bucket of footballs (claims). These footballs are different colors (payer IDs). Tom also throws these balls to receivers (insurances).

Since each of these colors signifies a unique payer ID and insurance provider, Tom knows which ball needs to be thrown to each receiver. It's really that simple, and guess what? If you have the wrong payer ID entered in your dental software for an insurance company, the electronic claim will not get there. Remember why data entry is so important?

If you are not using a clearinghouse or are looking for one that fits your practice, make your decision easy, compare the best dental clearinghouses out there, and understand the different functions of clearinghouses. Fully understanding dental claim submission[2] will ensure you are sending claims the correct way and being paid by insurance companies.

I've mentioned that you need a clearinghouse. This remains true. However, having a clearinghouse is moot unless you follow some basic claims submission guidelines:

1. Confirm your 2019 (the most current) ADA dental claim form is set up properly with correct billing and rendering provider information.

2. Pay attention to the dental codes you are using. They need to be accurate.

3. Your patient and patient insurance info need to be correct. No mistakes!

3. Insurance Carrier Processes and Pays Dental Claim

We are almost there! Hopefully, all of your dental claims pay, and you never have any issues. Sorry, but that would be a fairy tale. However, by taking the necessary steps you've read about so far, you should drastically limit the amount of unpaid or unprocessed claims. We'll discuss unpaid and unprocessed claims shortly.

Let's talk about the dental claims that do pay. Insurance carriers send payment in a few ways: virtual credit card (VCC), paper check, and electronic fund transfer (EFT). As a dental provider, you can essentially opt-in for whatever form of payment you want. What's important is making sure whatever you decide is the best fit for your office and dental team performing the billing.

Dental Virtual Credit Cards

VCCs[3] are printed on sheets of paper accompanying the explanation of benefits (EOB) provided by the insurance company. They show an image of a "credit card" including a credit card number, expiration date, and the exact dollar amount loaded on the card for the claim being paid. Beware! VCCs are also accompanied by the dreaded merchant fee. Do yourself a favor and opt-in for EFTs or continue to receive paper checks.

Dental Paper Check

Listen, I get it. In this day and age, why get a paper check when the way of the world has gone so digital? Also, there are other ways of being paid such as those VCCs we just discussed or EFTs. Well, simply put, nothing is "wrong" with check payments. A common misconception about check payments is that they take too long to actually receive. However, most insurance companies will get a paper check to you within 12–18 days. What's also funny is VCCs have to be mailed or faxed ... so how would they be that much more quickly received? They wouldn't, and they cost you merchant fees.

What's important is making sure you are comfortable with how you receive your payments. Fewer avenues of being paid typically lead to fewer mistakes in the accounting department. If you are comfortable with a slightly longer wait to receive payment, paper checks aren't going to hurt you. Another benefit is you don't have to track down an explanation of benefits when you receive a check payment as the two always accompany each other in the mail.

Dental Electronic Funds Transfer

EFTs have become the most popular form of insurance payment. Personally, it's easy to agree with this. EFTs are directly deposited into your business bank account, and the claim payments are much faster, usually outracing paper checks and VCCs by a week or more. Not all EFTs are created equal though,[4] and some insurance web portals are not as user-friendly as others.

With EFTs, you have to go to the insurance web portal from which you received the EFT in order to retrieve the electronic remittance advice (ERA/digital EOB). This is the only way you can actually post the dental claim payment. If you don't retrieve the ERA, then the claim is never posted, closing the claim out, yet you have actually received the funds in your bank account. That means the claims will still show as outstanding on your insurance aging report, inflating it.[5] Inflated reports are a common problem in dental offices.

Long story short, *be consistent with the way you receive payments*. If you only see one patient with a random insurance company named "X," don't opt-in for EFTs with "X" as this creates more work for your billing team. Just get paid by paper checks from that insurance. However, let's say you see tons of Cigna patients. Cigna would be good to opt-in for EFTs. The website is easy to navigate, and Cigna will pay many patients on one bulk EFT that hits the website every few days. Your billing team will know when to visit the website in order to post a large payment.

4. Posting the Insurance Payment in Your Dental Software

The final step of the dental billing process is posting the claim payment. Posting the payment does a few things for you:

1. It records the payment in your practice management software. All payments should match up directly with your deposit in your bank account.

2. Posting the claim payment applies a credit to the patient's ledger. The applied credit either leaves a balance owed by the patient that needs to be collected or hopefully creates a "0 balance."

3. It removes the claim from the insurance aging report as the claim is no longer "outstanding."

There is also an ideal way of posting insurance payments.

You Should Always Post Payments by Procedure

What does this mean? Posting payments by procedure means allocating exactly what was paid for each procedure/line item to the correct procedure and line item in your dental software. Posting by procedure offers four main benefits:[6]

1. Compensate your providers (dentists and hygienists) accurately and efficiently.

2. Know exactly what was paid for each procedure.

3. Maintain a current preferred provider organization (PPO) fee schedule.

4. Calculate the patient's portion and PPO provider write-off for dual insurance accurately.

No-Pays and Appeals

Some claims process but don't actually pay anything. That's not to say they were processed incorrectly, and we'll discuss that further. But as a dental biller, you should always make certain every claim is processed *accurately*. You also need to get as much reimbursement from the insurance company as possible for every procedure performed.

Claims that process but don't actually pay anything come in the form of no-pays or appeals.

What Is a No-Pay?

Your claim may be denied as a no-pay based on the provisions of the patient's dental plan. Each dental plan has limitations and exclusions. A no-pay is exactly what it sounds like. It's a dental claim that was processed correctly but no payment was sent because of various yet common exclusions and clauses. Below are just a few of the common reasons for claim denials:

- Frequency limitations
- Age limitations
- Deductible
- Annual max reached
- Waiting periods
- Missing tooth clause
- Replacement clause
- Inclusive services
- Non-covered services
- Timely filing

Example

A no-pay was received due to frequency limitation for a patient's third cleaning of the year. The insurance plan processed the claim correctly but denied the claim due to the plan only covering two cleanings per year.

In this example, insurance processed the claim correctly. However, since the patient is only allowed two covered cleanings in the benefit year, the third cleaning is processed accurately but no payment is sent. This particular claim would be posted to the patient's account as a $0 payment. The patient is only responsible for the contracted fee if the provider is in the network and the claim is closed out.

What Is an Appeal?

An appeal is a request to reconsider and reprocess a claim that has already been processed by the insurance company. Appeals are necessary if a claim is denied from insurance that you feel should have paid or a claim paid less than what you believe it should have.

A few common reasons you would want to send an appeal are for:

- Downgrades
- Alternate benefits
- Timely filing
- Medical necessity
- Any incorrect denials

Most importantly, appeals are inevitable but necessary. Insurance companies are the biggest buildings in any city you visit. Why? Because they deny claims!

It is our job as dental professionals to fight for the patients and get these claims paid. By this point, you probably understand the importance of the dental billing process, especially when it comes to insurance verification. So you being the smart person you are, you know that if a procedure should have been covered by insurance but wasn't, you need to figure out how to overturn that decision. Knowing how to win insurance appeals[7] will save your patients money and put insurance dollars in your office's pocket.

[1] dentalclaimsupport.com/blog/best-dental-clearinghouses

[2] dentalclaimsupport.com/blog/dental-claim-submission

[3] dentalclaimsupport.com/blog/virtual-credit-cards

[4] dentalclaimsupport.com/blog/not-all-efts-are-created-equal

[5] dentalclaimsupport.com/blog/is-your-insurance-aging-report-inflated

[6] dentalclaimsupport.com/blog/posting-by-procedure

[7] dentalclaimsupport.com/how-to-win-dental-insurance-appeals

3

Daily Deposit Report and Reconciliation

The Daily Deposit Report: Reconciliation of Payments

All payments posted to your dental software on any given day can be found on the daily deposit report. It's in the name of this report how often it should be run: *daily!* Your daily deposit report consists of all the various forms of payments made to your office on that workday. Although there are only two entities that pay your office (patients and insurance companies), payments can still come in many forms.

Patient payments can come via credit cards, patient checks, and cash. And insurance payments can come via the aforementioned virtual credit cards, insurance checks, and electronic funds transfers.

However you receive your funds, *what ends up in your bank account needs to match your deposit report in your dental software **to the penny***. That is the definition of reconciliation. Not running this report or reconciling your payments daily is a recipe for errors.

On the next page is an example daily deposit report. Strictly focusing on insurance payments, you can see that the two different payment types (checks and EFTs) have been split up on the report. For reconciliation purposes, this is exactly what you want to see.

As a dental biller, you would want to make sure that after adding all your insurance checks up, that number is exactly $3,705.87. Also, your EFT payments should total $6,096.05. These two numbers together give you a full deposit of $9,801.92. If this number doesn't match, you need to figure out why!

Remember how I said not running this report is a recipe for errors …

What if these insurance checks from the deposit report above were deposited into your bank account yet no one actually posted these payments in your dental software? Think about this. Payments not posted means claims are still open and showing as outstanding. That would mean your A/R reports still show you are owed money when, in actuality, you've already been paid. I see this all the time in offices that are struggling with their own dental billing processes.

Running your deposit report can also help pinpoint fraud or detect possible improprieties. No doctor ever wants to think they have a dishonest employee, but it happens. This report can catch things like a $100 cash payment being applied to a patient's ledger and showing on the deposit report, yet that $100 is not showing up in your bank account. Why? Because a dishonest employee stuffed it in his pocket! Protect yourself.

Daily Payments
Stringham Family Brand Toothy Ways
All Providers
All Clinics

Insurance Payments

Check

Date	Carrier	Patient Name	Provider	Clinic	Check#	Amount
02/28/2017	Aetna Galactic	Fry, Phillip J	HYG		9457615843	105.80
02/28/2017	Aetna Galactic	Fry, Phillip J	JEDI		9457615843	202.40
03/01/2017	Aetna Galactic	Krapapple, Edna	HYG		12311	105.80
03/01/2017	Aetna Galactic	Krapapple, Edna	JEDI		12311	202.40
03/01/2017	Aetna Galactic	Roderiguez, BenderB	HYG		7985263	105.80
03/01/2017	Aetna Galactic	Skinner, Seymour	HYG		546465	115.00
03/01/2017	Aetna Galactic	Skinner, Seymour	JEDI		546465	310.00
03/03/2017	Aetna Galactic	Cross, Rosemary	JEDI		65464684	430.00
03/06/2017	Lars' Grain and Homeopt	Hogger, Hogger	JEDI			40.00
03/10/2017	Aetna Galactic	Goober, Lance	HYG		32232	155.00
03/10/2017	Aetna Galactic	Goober, Lance	JEDI		32232	840.00
03/10/2017	Aetna Galactic	Nahasapeemapetilon, Ap	HYG		144	77.67
03/10/2017	Aetna Galactic	Nahasapeemapetilon, Ap	JEDI		144	100.00
03/10/2017	Aetna Galactic	Sampson, Brock	JEDI		8874	996.00
						3,705.87

EFT

Date	Carrier	Patient Name	Provider	Clinic	Check#	Amount
03/03/2017	Lars' Grain and Homeopt	Hogger, Hogger	HYG		12	74.00
03/03/2017	Lars' Grain and Homeopt	Hogger, Hogger	JEDI		12	231.00
03/09/2017	Aetna Galactic	Roderiguez, BenderB	JEDI		23132132	-4,344.05
03/15/2017	Tongue Bites and Street	Brannigan, Zapp	JEDI			49.09
03/15/2017	Aetna Galactic	Brannigan, Zapp	JEDI			80.68
03/15/2017	Aetna Galactic	Cross, Rosemary*	JEDI			1,317.40
						6,096.05

Total Insurance Payments: $9,801.92

You've now been through a smooth dental billing process, from a patient walking through your door to their claim getting paid and posted accurately. You also now know how important it is to run your daily deposit report and double-check what has been paid by patients and insurance companies is *exactly* what has shown up in your bank account.

What if the dental billing process wasn't completed in full? Not all dental claims pay automatically. Some may have been caught up in the clearinghouse and didn't get to the insurance company altogether. Some may have been received by the insurance company but needed additional information.

With claims that haven't been processed or paid, we have to research them and find out why. This is when we turn to the insurance aging report.

4

The Dental Insurance Aging Report

Working the Outstanding Insurance Aging Report: What If the Dental Claim Does Not Pay?

Although not a "step" in the dental bill-ing process, one of the main tasks your dental team should be performing is working the outstanding insurance aging report.[1] Working this report simply means researching claims that are 30 days old but have not been paid or processed.

An insurance aging report is a report composed of all outstanding dental claims created and sent to insurance companies.

Plainly put, these are dental claims not processed or paid by the insurance company and posted to patient account ledgers. Posting the processed claims and payments "closes" out the claim, which removes it from the insurance aging report.

In most practice management software, such as Dentrix®, OpenDental®, and Eaglesoft®, the insurance aging report setups are alike. The report lists all open claims by insurance carrier. It also sorts the claims by age, hence the name "aging" report. Someone in your office needs to know how to run the insurance aging report, understand it, and monitor it, *always*!

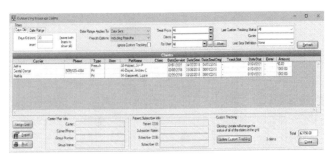

So, let's explain further.

For example, if you saw a patient today and created and sent a claim, that claim is zero days old. If the same claim has not been processed/paid in 30 days, meaning you don't have a deposit in your bank account or a check in your hand, that claim has aged 30 days. That claim needs to be researched.

Most dental billers call these claims "claims on your over-30-day report." This exact report should be run (printed and reviewed) and worked (claims researched) at least weekly.

The example image above shows three claims on the insurance aging report that have reached 30 days or older. These three claims would need to be researched in order to get them back into processing or push them through processing with the correct information.

Dental Claims 30 Days and Older Should Be Your Focus as a Dental Biller

Dental plans follow established prompt payment laws in most states. Depending on the type of plan, insurance payers legally have anywhere from 30–45 days to process a claim. In other words, there's no point in researching a claim that's 14 days old, as you'll probably find out the claim is in process and set to pay. Don't waste your time here.

Focus your time on claims over 30 days old that need actual attention and research. Yes, some people may disagree with me here. I hear of some dental billers that say, "I work claims that hit 14 days or more and haven't been paid!" To that I say, "Why?" There is so much to do in a dental office. Congratulations to anyone that doesn't have a claim over 30 days old, and if you don't, you probably aren't reading this!

However, when calling on or researching claims that are only 14 days old, you will find that many have either already paid and the money is in transit, or the claims are in processing and there isn't anything you can do.

Sure, you might come across one out of ten that needs additional attention or that isn't on file, but ask yourself this: Was your time value of money worth checking on ten claims and nothing being wrong with nine of them? The answer should be a resounding *no*.

I would say, though, if you are running your insurance aging reports for claims earlier than 30 days old, simply look for a trend.

Look for a date of service that sticks out. See if you notice an above-average amount of claims for the same insurance company or family that are outstanding.

If a date of service sticks out and has many unpaid claims, there could have been an issue with claim submission that day. Easy fix.

Do you see a lot of claims for the same insurance company or family? Most likely it's an issue with a payer ID for the insurance company or guarantor ID for a family. If you notice these trends, you can cut down on the time it takes you to work through all these claims. That is working smarter.

Back to the over-30-day report, as much as you don't want claims aging 30 days or more, it's almost inevitable. You can have the most fail-safe, buttoned-up process in place, but insurance companies are sticklers. They will find a way to deny certain claims.

Or in a time of amazing technology, sometimes things just don't work, and you have glitches. This could be either in processing at the insurance company level or processing in your own dental software or clearinghouse. That's why someone has to be dedicated to staying on top of this report.

There are proven techniques and principles to getting these claims processed though. Knowing how to decrease an insurance aging report, and doing it quickly, will ensure claims don't continue to age or be neglected altogether.

Research every claim on the over-30-day insurance aging report to find out why it's still there. When you are considering how long it will take to clean up the report, you must factor in the time, quality, and quantity.

- The *time* is in the research of talking to the insurance carrier, claim by claim. You can also utilize online portals to speed up the research of the claim status.

- The *quality* is in the questions asked and the knowledge of how to get claims paid. You then may believe your aging report cleanup is based on the dollar amount of the claims outstanding.

- The *quantity* of claims can best determine how long your cleanup will take.

How Do Claims Show Up on the Outstanding Dental Insurance Aging Report?

Remember this from earlier? *"Insurance verification is the single most important task you can perform in any dental office.* Why? Among many reasons *(more on this later)* ..."

It was only a matter of time until we got back to insurance verification and data entry. As stated earlier in the book, not completing these tasks is a surefire way for claims to consistently flood this aging report.

Insurance verification can be thought of as the most proactive way of working an insurance aging report. No, it's not "technically" working the report, but the more insurance is verified, the fewer rejections or delayed claims you have. This means fewer claims pop up on the insurance aging report. Taking the time to perform insurance verification will save you countless hours in the future of researching claims that should have never shown up on the report in the first place.

Not performing insurance verification isn't the only reason dental claims show up on the outstanding insurance aging report,[2] though. The more upfront measures your dental team can take to avoid unprocessed dental claims, the better chance your dental office has of being successful.

[1] dentalclaimsupport.com/blog/how-do-i-decrease-my-dental-insurance-aging-report

[2] dentalclaimsupport.com/blog/why-are-claims-on-my-dental-insurance-aging-report

5

Get It Done! Implement the Billing Process

There you have it. You now know the full dental billing process from start to finish. Nuances exist in every step, and experience is the best way to learn. Remember, simplify this. If you can take one patient through this dental billing process with success, there is no reason you shouldn't be able to take 100 or 1,000. That's the mindset your dental billing team needs to have.

Remember, this process will not perform on its own. There needs to be someone responsible, and held accountable, for every step along the way. The beauty of the process is, with time, you will be able to identify exactly where an issue lies. For instance, you will pinpoint if an issue lies between steps three and four or six and seven simply because the process works like a chain; identify the kink, and you've identified the problem.

So what's the best way to hold people accountable? When managing people or a process, there are two surefire ways to monitor:

1. Know when a task is supposed to be performed.

2. Measure if the task is being performed accurately.

Knowing when a task should be performed is easy. Simply create a schedule for those tasks, and ensure the person responsible for each task performs those duties during the allotted time.

Measuring if a task is performed accurately takes some more digging into raw data. The best way to monitor performance is to run reports in your dental software that tell you exactly how your office is performing. I will discuss this further in Part 2 of this book.

Create a Schedule for Your Process!

This may sound like overkill, but hear me out. It's safe to say the same offices that don't have a clearly defined dental billing process surely don't have a schedule for this process. Creating a schedule keeps your dental team on task. Everybody knows exactly what to do and when to do it. Having schedules is the most efficient way to perform any occupation at any type of business. Before you shy away from this premise, take a look at the sample process and schedule below.

Dental Biller's Schedule	Monday	Tuesday	Wednesday	Thursday	Friday
8-9	Claim Submission: Attachments and Clearinghouse rejections				
9-10	Insurance Verification (48 hours out)				
10-11					
11-12	Posting: Checks and VCCs	Posting: EFTs	Posting: Checks and VCCs	Posting: EFTs	No Pays/Appeals
12-1					
1-2	Lunch				
2-3	Insurance Aging Report	Insurance Aging Report	Insurance Aging Report	Insurance Aging Report	Have a great weekend!!!
3-4					
4-5			No pays/Appeals		

It is name-agnostic. You can see the tasks are nameless. Sure, you will have a "named" someone in your office performing these tasks. But what if that person left tomorrow, and you brought another employee in? The new employee should know exactly what to do and when to do it.

Don't stop with schedules and processes here. Create one for everything you do in the office. There should be a process and schedule for everything, such as:

- Ordering supplies
- Cleaning operatories
- Cleaning dental equipment
- Paying bills

Once the process is written, work with it, and fine-tune it. You will see that having these processes and a schedule for tackling them only helps your dental team in staying focused and on task.

Many dental offices have been able to adapt the dental billing process and run with it smoothly. However, many other offices have felt the headache and continue to search for help. This is simple stuff, but it's hard to do. If you find your team struggling to keep up, or simply don't have the time or the right team in place to handle your dental billing, you need to consider other options.

Don't let deficiencies in your dental billing process snowball into an insurmountable problem. Outsourced dental billing has helped multiple dentists across the United States and could be a viable option for you. It has become a norm in modern dental offices today. With a rapid switch to remote work and advancements in technology, dental billing can be done at an expert level from home. Keep your options open and do what's best for you and your dental team. Visit dentalclaimsupport.com for more information on outsourced dental billing and determine if it's a viable option for you and your team.

BONUS: Remember to visit our website at bonus.dentalbillingandreporting.com to get special bonuses to help you build your practice, just for reading this book.

Part 2

Dental Reporting

6

The Dental Revenue Cycle

Running a smooth dental office doesn't end at moving patients through your operatories and getting claims paid. Part 1 was all about the dental billing process, but you also need to fully understand how your office is performing.

The absolute best way is to understand your revenue cycle and focus on key performance indicators (KPIs), or key reports, that literally speak to the health of your dental business.

Your KPIs can be broken down into the revenue chart below:

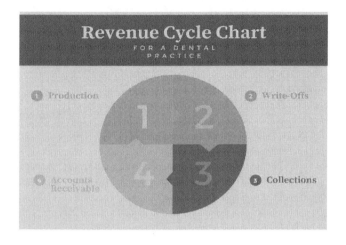

As you can see, the key reports you need to run and understand in your dental office are the:

1. Production report
2. Write-offs report
3. Collections report
4. A/R report

Starting with production and ending with A/R, I will break down each report, what it means, and what you need to understand about it. I will be providing example reports from the OpenDental® software for visuals.

By the end of Part 2, you should be able to run your own reports and see where you may be inefficient or, hopefully, where you are killing it!

Before diving in, it's beneficial to understand these important items:

- Production - Write-offs = Net Production
    - Net production is what you are *truly* owed.

- Collections / Net Production = *Collection Percentage*
    - Collection percentage means what percentage of what you are truly owed have you collected.
    - The national collection percentage average is 91%.

Collection percentage is one of the best KPIs to track in your office. Your office should not strive for a 91% collection percentage. You should strive for 100%. Understanding how to achieve the highest collection percentage possible[1] is critical to your bottom line and can save your practice.

[1] dentalclaimsupport.com/blog/increase-your-dental-practice-collections-percentage

7

Important Reports You Will *Own*

1. Dental Production Report

It all begins with production. You have to produce in order to collect. A production report can be run in any practice management software to analyze production by day, month, or year. Production refers to any procedures performed on a patient and carries a dollar value.

An easy example would be a crown performed for $1,000. For every crown performed, you produce $1,000. If all procedures performed in a month added up to $100,000, then your production for the month is $100,000.

Knowing your production month to month is important. If you consistently are producing $100,000 on average per month, then suddenly start producing only $70,000, you need to figure out why.

- Are patients dropping off your schedule?

- Has your production from major services such as crowns, implants, or bridges died down?

If you aren't running this report, you may not notice the downward trend. If you don't notice the downward trend, you won't even realize that your production has fallen $30k per month or $360k per year. That would be detrimental to your dental practice.

2. Write-Off Report and Net Production

Your write-off report is important as it indicates how much money is actually subtracted from your total production. Write-off reports can be run in any software management system by day, month, or year. A "write-off" is essentially any amount credited to the patient for any number of reasons.

Two common examples of write-offs include insurance write-offs and professional courtesies.

Example Write-Off Report:

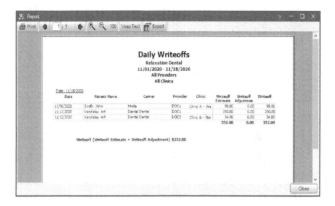

Insurance Write-Offs

Many dentists participate with insurance companies. When you participate with an insurance company, you agree to accept that insurance company's fee schedule. This means you can only charge a patient covered by that insurance a specific negotiated fee associated with each procedure.

For example, let's say you have a Metlife patient coming in for a cleaning, and you participate with Metlife. The standard fee you would charge a cash patient or a patient with an out-of-network insurance is $100. However, you are in-network with Metlife, and their negotiated fee for a cleaning is $70. In this instance, you can only charge that patient $70 and $30 would have to be written off (write-off)

$$100 - \$70 = \$30 \text{ write-off}$$

Therefore, $100 - $30 write-off = $70

In this case, your true *net production is $70,* not $100.

Professional Courtesies

These write-offs consist of anything you agree not to charge to a patient for any particular reason. Maybe the patient had a bad experience. Maybe the patient is a family member or friend. Maybe the patient is a veteran, and you give discounts to veterans. Regardless, whatever courtesy or discount you give will "take away" from your production.

An example would be charging a cash patient $100 for a cleaning, but giving a 10% discount because they are a veteran:

$100 x 10% discount = $10 discount/write-off

Therefore, $100 - $10 write-off = $90

In this case, your true *net production is $90*, not $100

So in both of these examples, it's important to know what your true net production really is. Take the two examples from above and add them together. Do you have your number?

The thing is, I have heard many doctors, even with those two example procedures, say that their production is $200. This is incorrect. The true (net) production is actually $160, not $200, because of the $30 and $10 write-offs.

$200 - $40 (write-offs) = *$160 net production*

Sorry, more math ... Since you have $40 in write-offs in this example, that means your write-offs total 20% of your full production.

$40 / $200 = 20% in write-offs

Track this number! If you typically have an average write-off percentage of 20%, and it starts to rise to 30% or 40%, you need to figure out why. Validate that your dental team isn't writing off what you are truly owed. Then confirm your team is collecting on insurance claims and patient balances and not just writing off what they haven't fought to get paid.

3. Collections Report and Collection Percentage

You need to know the revenue coming into your practice. Collections in a dental practice come from two entities: the insurance companies and your patients. Coordinating insurance and patient payments can be a very tough task, but you need to know exactly what you are collecting in your practice from insurance companies and patients.

The collections report can be run by day, month, year, or any length of time you choose. Remember, you should be running your collection report daily for reconciliation purposes.

Now that you understand your net production and what you are truly owed, you can figure out if your team is collecting payments sufficiently. The best way to know if your team is hitting target numbers is to understand your collection percentage.

Collections Percentage

I stated earlier that the national collection percentage for dental offices is around 91%. Think about that for a second. Does that number sound good to you? Here's a clear-cut example for you to mull over.

We know that your collection percentage is a simple equation:

$$\textit{Collections / Net Production} = \textit{Collection Percentage}$$

To achieve the average collection rate in the U.S., think of your office as producing $1 million in services. To hit the average your office numbers would be:

*$910,000 (collections) / $1,000,000
(net production) = 91% (collection percentage)*

This means that the average million-dollar dental practice in our nation loses out on collecting $90,000/year or $7,500/month. This should not be the case, but it is. I'm sure you could think of plenty of ways you could use an extra $90,000 per year.

Lost revenue occurs because a clearly defined dental billing process isn't in place to follow and execute. Think about if this practice only collected $800,000 a year … That would be a collection percentage of 80%. Can you imagine not collecting on $200,000 owed to you that should be in your pocket?

Let's get back to the 91% national average. Where is the other 9%? That should be the question you ask yourself after you find out your own collection percentage. Where is the other uncollected percentage, and how do I get that money in my pocket?

The other "9%" is wrapped up in your A/R reports. Let's take a look.

4. Accounts Receivable Reports: Patient A/R and Insurance A/R

All insurance and patient amounts owed to you in your practice can be found on the accounts receivable reports.

Most dental software has the ability to run this report as a total, meaning all money owed to the dental practice by patients *and* insurance companies. Or you can run the accounts receivable reports separately. You can run the patient A/R report *or* the insurance aging report.

Take a look at the sample aging report below. Keep in mind this is a "total" A/R report, meaning it's made up of balances owed to your office by patients *and* insurance companies.

AGING OF ACCOUNTS RECEIVABLE

Relaxation Dental
As of 08/06/2018
Any Balance
All Billing Types
All Providers
All Clinics

Date 08/06/2018

Guarantor	0-30 Days	31-60 Days	61-90 Days	> 90 Days	Total	-W/O Est	-Ins Est	=Patient
129 - Claim Payment, Patr:	0.00	50.00	0.00	0.00	50.00	0.00	0.00	50.00
122 - Clinic A, Patient	0.00	0.00	0.00	1,000.00	1,000.00	0.00	0.00	1,000.00
131 - Cometta, Hailey	0.00	0.00	265.00	0.00	265.00	0.00	0.00	265.00
69 - Discount , Plan	0.00	0.00	220.00	0.00	220.00	0.00	0.00	220.00
45 - Dwyer, April C	0.00	43.06	0.00	3,445.00	3,486.06	0.00	0.00	3,488.06
24 - Family , Dad	0.00	6.60	0.00	428.00	434.60	0.00	0.00	434.60
79 - Gaspereth, Gary	0.00	1,255.00	1,000.00	3,400.00	5,655.00	250.00	0.00	5,405.00
136 - Gonzalez, Brennan	2,482.00	0.00	0.00	0.00	2,482.00	340.00	1,046.00	1,096.00
132 - Grayson, Jack	0.00	160.00	359.00	0.00	519.00	0.00	0.00	519.00
100 - Groundrunner, Luke	0.00	69.00	0.00	0.00	69.00	0.00	0.00	69.00
89 - Insurance, Medical PP	0.00	0.00	0.00	1,880.00	1,880.00	0.00	0.00	1,880.00
61 - Jones, Gordon	0.00	315.00	0.00	66.00	381.00	0.00	0.00	381.00
66 - Mathison, Dolores C	0.00	17.08	0.00	1,366.00	1,383.06	0.00	0.00	1,383.08
76 - Medical, Insurance	0.00	12.50	0.00	1,000.00	1,012.50	0.00	0.00	1,012.50
119 - Moore, Harrison	1,285.00	247.00	0.00	0.00	1,532.00	99.00	148.00	1,285.00
76 - Ortho, Aurora	0.00	10.00	0.00	800.00	810.00	0.00	0.00	810.00
134 - Outstanding, Emma	0.00	0.00	0.00	500.00	500.00	0.00	0.00	500.00
15 - Peabody, Jack P	0.00	193.58	1,886.00	0.00	2,079.58	340.00	1,071.00	668.58
83 - Plan, Payment	0.00	1,350.00	0.00	0.00	1,350.00	0.00	0.00	1,350.00
103 - Plan, Treatment	0.00	650.00	0.00	0.00	650.00	0.00	0.00	650.00
117 - Skellar, Jackson	0.00	10.00	0.00	800.00	810.00	0.00	0.00	810.00
40 - Smith, Dwight	0.00	26.00	0.00	0.00	26.00	0.00	0.00	26.00
107 - Superfam, Allie	0.00	12.50	0.00	1,000.00	1,012.50	0.00	0.00	1,012.50
108 - Superfam, Beatrice	0.00	12.69	0.00	1,015.00	1,027.69	0.00	0.00	1,027.69
	3,767.00	4,440.01	3,730.00	16,700.00	28,637.01	1,029.00	2,265.00	25,343.01

Many offices often confuse the aging report with the insurance aging report. These are two different reports. Remember, in Chapter 4, we strictly discussed the insurance aging report, but since two entities pay your dental practice, you cannot solely focus on one or the other.

Both reports are equally important. Let's discuss why.

Let's say you are owed the $90,000 from the above example. Where is this money? If you run your patient A/R report and are only owed $10,000 from patients, then naturally you are owed the other $80,000 from insurance companies.

What should this tell you?

It should tell you that you need to work your insurance aging report. Remember, working the insurance aging report simply means researching all outstanding claims that have not been paid or processed.

If the numbers were flip-flopped, meaning patients owed your dental office $80,000 and outstanding insurance was only $10,000, then that means your dental team needs to work on getting patients to pay their balances. Nothing too crazy, right?

8

You Got This! Keep It Simple

You have probably thought a few times throughout this book, "You know, this isn't that difficult. Why haven't I looked at it this simply before? I can do this, no problem." *Yes, you can!*

Keep it simple. Do not overthink anything in dental billing and reporting. Stick to a process with everything in your dental practice, and know what truly drives your practice. *Your patients drive your practice.*

You have all the skills to make your patients happy. You also now have the know-how to fight for them and drive revenue into your dental practice from insurance companies. Now take a deep breath, and get after it!

Common Dental Terms and Definitions

Below are some common dental terms and definitions you may have seen throughout this book. They come up every day in dental offices. Stay familiar with these terms and understand how they affect your dental practice.

- **Adjudication**: The automated processing of a claim with or without review.

- **Allowable Charge**: The maximum amount of benefit allowed for a dental procedure per the indemnity or the PPO plan contract.

- **Alternate Benefit**: A provision of a dental plan allowing the payer to provide a less expensive benefit or a lower reimbursement for a non-covered procedure. For example, the payer reimburses for an amalgam restoration when the doctor actually performed a composite restoration on a molar.

- **Assignment of Benefits**: Authorization by the patient for dental plan benefits to be paid directly to the provider of the service.

- **Audit**: A review of records by a payer to ensure providers are upholding responsibilities regarding plan specifications, along with applicable federal and state laws. Any violation found during an audit could result in the payer's request for repayment of funds paid to the doctor, sanctions, being dropped as a contracted provider, or referral to a state dental board for further review.

- **Birthday Rule**: Used to determine the primary payer of benefits for dependents when covered by both parents' plans. Only the month and day of the birthday are used to determine which parent's plan is the primary payer of benefits. Whichever parent's birth date falls first in the calendar year is primary, regardless of age. If both parents have the same DOB, then the plan that has covered the parent longer is primary.

- **By Report**: A brief narrative describing the dental procedure performed, required when reporting the CDT codes that have the words "by report" in the nomenclature.

- **Children's Health Insurance Program (CHIP)**: Provides health coverage to eligible children through both Medicaid and separate CHIP programs. CHIP is administered by states, according to federal requirements. The program is jointly funded by states and the federal government.

- **Clearinghouse**: A private or public company that provides connectivity and often serves as a "middleman" between healthcare providers and payers. Clearinghouses ensure that claims sent from your dental software are distributed to the correct insurance company electronically.

- **Coordination of Benefits (COB)**: The method of determining the order of benefits and payments when a patient is covered by more than one insurance plan intended to ensure that the total amount paid by all sources does not exceed the total fee submitted on the claim form by the practice.

- **Current Dental Terminology (CDT)**: A code set defined by the American Dental Association (ADA) that doctors are required to follow when reporting dental procedures to an insurance company for reimbursement and on patient billing statements.

- **Current Procedural Terminology (CPT)**: A code set defined by the American Medical Association (AMA) that medical and dental providers are required to follow when reporting medical procedures (on a medical claim form) to an insurance company for reimbursement and on patient billing statements.

- **Deductible**: The amount you must pay out of pocket each year before your plan starts to pay for covered dental treatment costs. Common deductibles in dental are anywhere from $50–$100 a patient.

- **Dental Benefits Consultant**: A licensed doctor who reviews dental claims for medical necessity and makes a recommendation regarding payment to the insurance payer based upon benefit guidelines per the dental plan document.

- **Discount Plan**: A plan offered by insurance companies at a set fee, allowing purchasers to receive discounted rates. A doctor may also offer an in-house discount plan offering a flat discount rate or package of services.

- **Electronic Remittance Advice (ERA)**: Basically, this is the same as an EOB but in digital form, not paper form. It explains the benefit paid for a claim and how the benefits(s) were determined.

- **Exclusions**: Procedures that are excluded from payment of benefits, as outlined in the plan document

- **Explanation of Benefits (EOB)**: Document received from the insurance payer when processing of a claim has been completed. The EOB explains the benefit paid and how the benefit was determined. If an EOB is from a PPO, it also explains the patient's financial responsibility.

- **FEDVIP**: The Federal Employee Dental and Vision Benefits Enhancement Act of 2004 provided the U.S. Office of Personnel Management (OPM) the opportunity to establish arrangements under which dental and vision benefits are made available to federal employees, retirees, and their dependents.

- **Fee Schedule**: A list of the set amount considered for each covered or non-covered procedure as outlined by an insurance company. It also refers to the amount charged by the practice for each procedure performed.

- **Fraud**: Occurs when an individual receives benefits paid by an insurance plan due to the filing of false claims, inflated claim, or the billing of services not actually performed. Fraud is determined by a court of law.

- **Frequency**: The number of procedures permitted during a specific period (i.e., 1 x 12 months, 2 per year, 2 every 12 months)

- **Gender Rule**: This rule establishes the order of benefits when children are covered by both parents' dental benefits. Under this rule, the father's policy is considered primary and will pay the claims of dependent children first.

- **Health Maintenance Organization (HMO)**: A legal entity that agrees to accept the financial risk and responsibility of providing specific services to a defined number of people over a specified time period for a fixed price. Patients of the HMO receive comprehensive care from assigned providers. In return for health care services, enrollees are usually assessed a monthly payment and may be obligated to stay in the program for the duration of the benefit period.

- **Informed Consent**: Consent from the patient to proceed with treatment after being presented with all necessary information to make an informed decision regarding such treatment.

- **Least Expensive Alternative Treatment (LEAT)**: A clause within a dental plan contract that allows the payer to provide the benefit of the least expensive alternative treatment option when multiple options of treatment are acceptable. For example, a benefit for a partial denture in lieu of a benefit for implants or fixed partial dentures when multiple teeth are missing in the arch are restored.

- **Maximum Allowable Benefit**: The total annual amount of benefits paid by the payer per patient.

- **Maximum Plan Allowance (MPA)**: The maximum benefit allowance of a procedure per the dental plan.

- **Medicaid**: A joint federal and state program that helps with healthcare costs for people with low income and limited resources. Medicaid programs vary by state.

- **Medicare**: The federal health insurance program for people 65 years of age or older, certain younger people with disabilities, and people with end-stage renal disease.

- **Missing Tooth Clause**: A provision of a dental plan explanation that insurance will not cover the cost of the replacement procedure if the tooth extracted or was already missing before the current coverage began for the patient. This can be thought of almost as a pre-existing condition.

- **Modifier**: CPT modifiers are two-digit codes used to provide additional information about the service provided.

- **Non-Duplication of Benefits**: A provision in an insurance policy specifying that benefits will not be provided for amounts reimbursed by other plans.

- **Plan Document**: Document outlining the details of the plan, including exclusions, limitations, etc. This document can be up to 200 pages and may only be obtained by the employee from the Human Resources Department if it is an employer-sponsored group plan or from the insurance company if an individual policy.

- **Point of Service (POS)**: A type of managed care plan that is a hybrid of HMO and PPO plans. Like an HMO, participants designate in-network physicians or dentists as their primary care providers. But, like a PPO, patients may go outside of the provider network for healthcare services.

- **Pre-Authorization**: A claim submitted prior to treatment to determine if the service will be a covered benefit by the patient's plan. Pre-auths involve dental benefits consultant review and approval for payment. Pre-auth is a guarantee of payment if the patient is eligible on the date of service. This is not the same as predetermination.

- **Predetermination**: A claim submitted to verify eligibility and benefits for proposed treatment prior to the start of treatment. Predetermination of eligibility and benefits does not guarantee payment.

- **Preferred Provider Organization (PPO)**: A network of dental providers who have a current contractual agreement to provide insured members with services at a reduced rate. PPO plans allow the patient to choose a provider outside the network. However, this may result in a reduction of reimbursement, or in some cases a higher fee.

- **Pretreatment Estimate**: A request submitted by the practice prior to the start of treatment to obtain an estimate of benefits, typically including the maximum allowed charge, expected benefit from the patient's plan, and the patient's responsibility. Pretreatment estimates do not guarantee payment.

- **Processing Policy Manual**: Policies, restrictions, and rules outlined by payers in a manual that contracted providers must follow in addition to the contract.

- **Protected Health Information (PHI)**: Information regarding a patient's health care is considered protected information under HIPAA. This includes, but is not limited to, clinical and financial information regarding the patient's health care and patient demographics.

- **Remapping (Downcoding)**: A practice by payers whereby the least expensive alternative treatment (LEAT) benefit is provided.

- **Replacement Clause**: A clause in over 90% of dental plans that states that the insurance will not pay for the replacement of existing prosthetics, such as crowns, dentures, and bridges until a certain time has passed. Most replacement clauses are anywhere from 5–10 years.

- **Schedule of Benefits**: A list of dental services and the maximum dollar benefit a payer will reimburse for a given service. The plan document of each payer lists the schedule of benefits and will vary based on the coverage of the plan.

- **Security Rule (HIPAA)**: Standard set of rules to be followed by covered entities and business associates that protect and ensure the security, confidentiality, and integrity of electronic information containing protected health information.

- **Take Back Procedure**: Describes a reduced benefit of a definitive procedure when a previous procedure has already been paid on a prior date of service. Usually, both procedures are performed by the same billing office. For example, a protective restoration (filling) is paid and then a subsequent crown is performed a few weeks later. The filling benefit is then subtracted from the crown benefit.

- **Third-Party Administrator (TPA)**: Responsible for the collection of payment from the employer, determination of benefits, and processing of benefits payments for claims.

- **TRICARE**: A health program for active duty and guard/reserve members and their families, their survivors, former spouses, Medal of Honor recipients and their families, and others registered in the Defense Enrollment Eligibility Reporting System.

- **Unclaimed Property**: Property or money held by the practice that it does not have legal ownership of. Every state has its own unclaimed property office and separate reporting requirements for unclaimed property.

- **Usual, Customary, and Reasonable (UCR)**: Average fees charged by a doctor in a specific region or zip code for procedures. UCR is calculated by payers using data obtained from fees submitted on claim forms by doctors from specific regions. Most commonly, the zip code determines the allowable fee.

- **Utilization Review**: A review by the payer of frequent procedures reported by a provider. This review is sometimes used to audit the provider to ensure accurate reporting or procedures and to detect overutilization or overbilling.

- **Waiting Period**: A time period starting on the effective date of coverage as stated within the patient's plan document, which must be satisfied prior to receiving benefits. This waiting period is usually a period of six to twelve months for basic and major classification or services.

There's more to help you master dental insurance billing and protect and grow your practice. Get your special bonus content at bonus.dentalbillingandreporting.com.

Made in the USA
Las Vegas, NV
05 September 2023

77082533R00065